MW00907451

Go Fish

Seven Speaking and Listening Games
for Learning Languages

Shawn Halwas

PRO LINGUA ASSOCIATES

Pro Lingua Associates, Publishers

P.O. Box 1348. Brattleboro, Vermont 05302-1348 USA
Office: 802 257 7779; Orders: 800 366 4775
Fax: 802 257 5117
WebStore: www.ProLinguaAssociates.com
Email: info@ProLinguaAssociates.com
       orders@ProLinguaAssociates.com
SAN: 216-0579

At Pro Lingua
our objective is to foster an approach
to learning and teaching that we call
interplay, the **inter**action of language
learners and teachers with their materials,
with the language and culture,
and with each other in active, creative
and productive **play.**

Copyright © 2007 by Shawn Halwas

ISBN 0-86647-238-X

All rights reserved. Except as noted below, no part of this publication may be reproduced or transmitted in any form or by any means, electronic, mechanical, photocopying, recording or other, or stored in an information storage or retrieval system without permission in writing from the publisher.

Teachers may photocopy the vocabulary list *(page v)*, the Bingo board *(page x)*, and the illustrations of additional vocabulary *(page 173 and 175)* for classroom use.

The illustrations of the rooms of the house are by Patrick R, Moran, The rest of the images are clipart from www.GraphicsFactory.com; *The Big Box of Art™*, Copyright 1997-2002 by Hermera Technologies Inc. and its licensors, and *Art Explosion®: 750,000 Images*, Copyright 1995-2000 by Nova Development Corporation and its licensors.

This book was set in Baskerville, a graceful, reserved Neoclassical typeface designed by John Baskerville in the mid-1750's in Birmingham, England. His training as a calligrapher is suggested by his flowing line and sharp serifs, but these are balanced with the clarity typical of the rationalist early 18th Century. The resulting face, beautiful and yet easy to read, remains popular into the digital age. The text and cover designs are by Arthur A. Burrows. Printing and binding arranged by Boyd Printing in Albany, N.Y.

First edition, first printing 2007. 1500 copies in print.

Contents

Other Pro Lingua game materials

Superphonic Bingo
The Great Big Bingo Book
The Great Big Book of Crosswords
Pronunciation Card Games
Shenanigames
Discovery Trail
Solo, Duo, Trio
Families
Play 'n Talk
Index Card Games
More Index Card Games
Match It

Vocabulary lists in other languages matching the vocabulary cards and additional vocabulary are available for free at ProLinguaAssociates.com.

Go Fish – the vocabulary

There are four sets of cards. **A, B,** and **C** each have 26 words (pairs) and **D** has 8 words (pairs).

There are nine numbered vocabulary topics: **1** Rooms in the home, **2** General vocabulary, **3** Kitchen, **4** Living room, **5** Dining room, **6** Bedroom, **7** Den, **8** Bathroom, **9** Kitchen non-count nouns

In this book, the cards appear by set **(ABCD)** and within the sets by topic (A-1, A-2).

1 *Rooms*
- kitchen *A-1*
- living room *A-2*
- bedroom *A-3*
- bathroom *A-4*
- dining room *A-5*
- study *A-6*
- basement *C-1*
- attic *C-2*
- garage *C-3*
- porch *C-4*

2 *General*
- door *A-7*
- window *A-8*
- lamp *A-9*
- light *A-10*
- switch *A-11*
- roof *B-1*
- ceiling *B-2*
- floor *B-3*
- wall *B-4*
- door knob *B-5*

3 *Kitchen*
- stove *A-12*
- sink *A-13*
- refrigerator *A-14*
- toaster *B-6*
- microwave *B-7*
- dishwasher *B-8*
- mixer *B-9*
- trash can *C-5*
- pot *C-6*
- frying pan *C-7*
- carving knife *C-8*
- spatula *C-9*

4 *Living room*
- sofa *A-15*
- easy chair *A-16*
- coffee table *A-17*
- television *B-10*
- DVD player *B-11*
- book *B-12*
- bookshelf *B-13*
- rug *B-14*

5 *Dining room*
- dining room table *A-18*
- chair *A-19*
- glass *B-15*
- fork *B-16*
- spoon *B-17*
- knife *B-18*
- plate *B-19*
- bowl *B-20*
- cup *B-21*

6 *Bedroom*
- bed *A-20*
- bureau *A-21*
- blanket *A-22*
- closet *C-10*
- hanger *C-11*
- pillow *C-12*
- sheet *C-13*
- mirror *C-14*
- shade *C-15*

7 *Den/study/office*
- desk *A-23*
- telephone *A-24*
- newspaper *C-16*
- cabinet *C-17*
- laptop *C-18*
- printer *C-19*
- sound system *C-20*

8 *Bathroom*
- bathtub *A-25*
- basin *A-26*
- toilet *B-22*
- shower *B-23*
- washcloth *B-24*
- towel *B-25*
- faucet *B-26*
- scale *C-21*
- comb *C-22*
- brush *C-23*
- razor *C-24*
- shaver *C-25*
- toothbrush *C-26*

9 *Kitchen non-count nouns*
- flour *D-1*
- soap *D-2*
- milk *D-3*
- ice *D-4*
- soup *D-5*
- bread *D-6*
- butter *D-7*
- meat *D-8*

> *Set A – 26 words, 52 cards*
> *Set B – 26 words, 52 cards*
> *Set C – 26 words, 52 cards*
> *Set D – 8 words, 16 cards*

> 10 additional vocabulary items are illustrated on pages 173 and 175. These may be copied, cut out, pasted on blank cards, and used to play any of the seven games.

Introduction
The Game Cards

All the vocabulary used in these games are names of items found around the house. The cards in this book illustrate 86 different words, each on two cards (172 cards). To add interest, the two illustrations of each word are different. The entire list of 86 lexical items is subdivided into 9 sub-sets. *(See page v.)* These cards can be used for a variety of activities and games, and they can be used for play in virtually any language because the lexical items are pictured without written words on the cards. Of course, if an illustrated item is not known or recognized in the target culture and language, it need not be used. To supplement the 86 words, 40 additional vocabulary items are pictured *(pages 173 and 175)*. To make pairs of cards, photocopy and cut the pictures out, and paste them on blank cards.

Playing the Seven Games

Go Fish

This version of **Go Fish** can be enjoyed by learners of all ages. Although it is most suitable for learners at a low proficiency level, even intermediate and advanced learners can enjoy the game while developing their language skills, especially in the give-and-take of discourse.

To play **Go Fish,** you need one set of 52 cards (26 pairs of cards/26 words). In this book there are three complete sets of 26 pairs (78 different words). The words in these complete sets can be found on page *v*, indicated by color. The first set is red, the second blue, the third green. However, you are not limited to these sets. The cards can be mixed and matched to produce a variety of different sets. For example, you can make a set including all the bedroom and bathroom vocabulary. There is also a fourth, short set of 8 nouns (16 cards), listed in black. These can be used as "wild cards" to force the players to distinguish between count and noncount nouns in English *(Do you have a chair?* vs *Do you have any fruit?)*

Having three complete sets of cards, allows the class to play **Go Fish** at least three different times using entirely different cards/words. Or you can have three different groups playing with three different sets at the same time.

Because the game is best played with groups of four players, the three full sets of cards allow at least 12 players to be playing **Go Fish** at the same time. In classes where there may be more than twelve students, have the students play as teams of two. The pairs, acting as a team, can consult on who and what to ask for.

Go Fish can be played mainly as a vocabulary activity, helping learners practice seeing and saying a few words. However, the game also offers learners an opportunity to practice speaking and listening as they play the game. In fact, this "peripheral" aspect of the game may be more important than the activity of identifying a limited number of lexical items.

You can also require the players to use particular grammatical structures while playing the game. For example, a basic exchange in English could be:

Please give me a _____. *(imperative)*
Please take this. or ***Go fish!***

These are simple structures, but there are many common variations that could be used. For example:

To Ask:

Would you please give me a _____?
I would like to have a _____.
Do you have a _____?
I need a _____.
I want a _____. Do you have one?*
I think you are holding a _____. Am I right?*
May I have a _____.
Would you mind giving me your _____?
Don't you have any _____s?*
I'm fishing for a _____.
etc.

Responses can be:

You are lucky, I have a _____.
Is this what you want?
OK, you can have my _____.
OK, but show me your _____ first.*
Congratulations! You caught a _____.
I just happen to have a _____.

Or:

Sorry, I don't have one/a _____.
No, I have no _____s.*
Sorry, there aren't any in my hand.
You've asked the wrong person.
You should ask somebody else.
Sorry! Take a fish from the pool.

The students should also be encouraged to ad lib (in the target language, of course) as they play.

Match It

Choose 12 pairs of cards and mix them up. Then place them on a large table or the floor in a grid of 6 columns and 4 rows. With blank cards or pieces of paper label the columns 1-6 and the rows A-D, as indicated below:

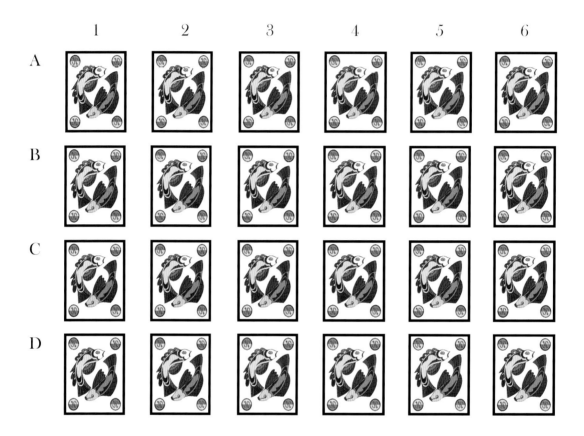

The players (as individuals or pairs or triads) try to locate matching pairs. Player 1 calls out B4. A game host turns over B4 revealing the picture. Player 1 tries to find a match.

Player 1 :	***B4*** (a toaster is revealed)
	I need a toaster. **C6** (a stove is revealed)
Game Host:	***Sorry, no match.*** (***B4*** and **C6** are turned face down)
Player 2:	***A3*** (a stove is revealed)
	Aha! I have two stoves! **C6.** (the two stoves are matched)

When a match is made the pair of cards is removed and given to the player who matched the two cards. After a match is made it is better to have the play go to the next player. Otherwise, as the game nears a close, one player will monopolize the matching.

Flash Card Games

Quiz Game: A simple game is to divide the class into teams. You flash a card at Team 1. They try to identify the card. You can have them simply name it or use it in a sentence, or as in Jeopardy, have them form a question (What is a toaster?). If they fail to respond correctly, Team 2 gets a chance to respond, and so forth.

Spelling Bee: Divide the class into teams. Flash a card at a team. They have to spell it correctly using oral spelling: _Ceiling is see–ee–ay–el–ay–en–gee._

Pattern Practice: Establish a basic sentence or simple exchange that requires the correct use of one or more grammatical points.

> Example: _I don't have a/any _____. I wish I did. Do you have one/some? No, I don't have a/any _____._

Flash a card, and the student or students have to respond with the pattern correctly. This is a simple repetition practice, but a little more fun than a pattern or substitution drill.

Pantomime/20 Questions: The students are each given a card. They cannot show their cards to their classmates. They can pantomime their words, as in charades, or to make the game more challenging, they can be limited to answering only yes or no to their classmates' questions. Since the number of items on the cards is limited, it may be better to limit the questions to five. If they can't guess after five questions, they do not get a point.

Bingo

Copy the list on page iii and give one to each student. Give them a copy of the blank 16-square grid on page x. You may want to proscribe the list to one of the sets or one or two of the rooms/places. Have the students choose 16 words and write them in the squares. Then mix up the cards that are appropriate for the list you are using and place them in a pile. As in other Bingo games, take cards from the pile one at a time and call out the item until someone makes four in a row across, up-and-down or diagonally.

A Suggested Sequence of Games

In the back of the book there is a five-day sequence that can be followed to introduce and continue to use the cards and play **Go Fish** effectively.

Go Fish Bingo!

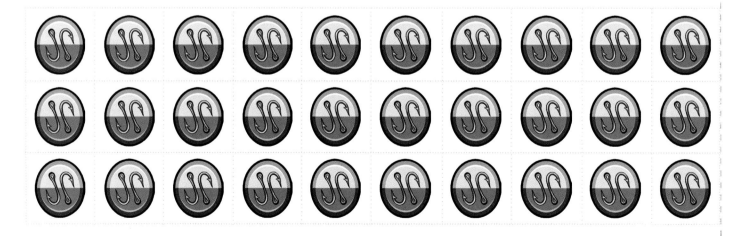

x

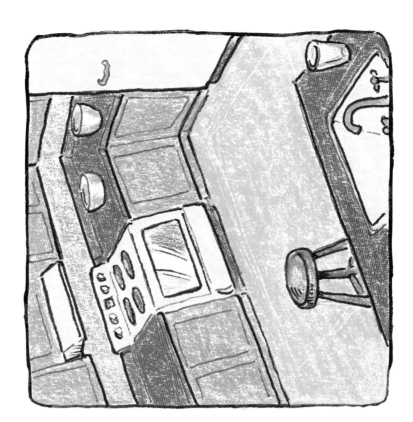

A-1

A-1

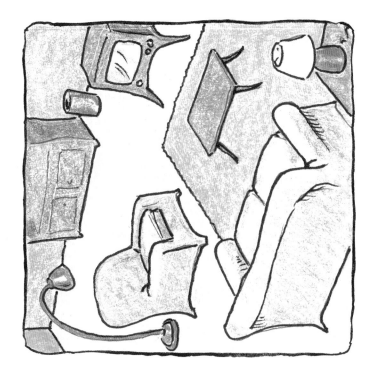

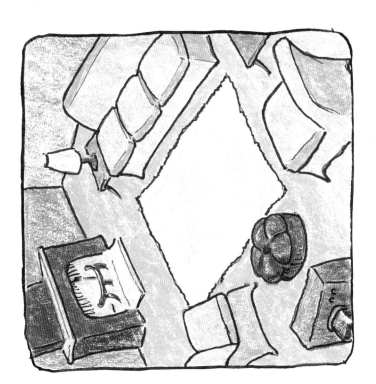

A-3

A-3

A-4

A-4

A-6

A-6

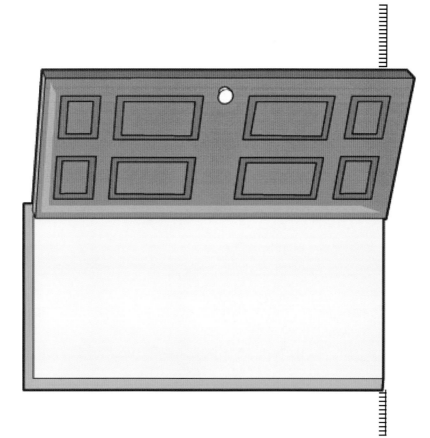

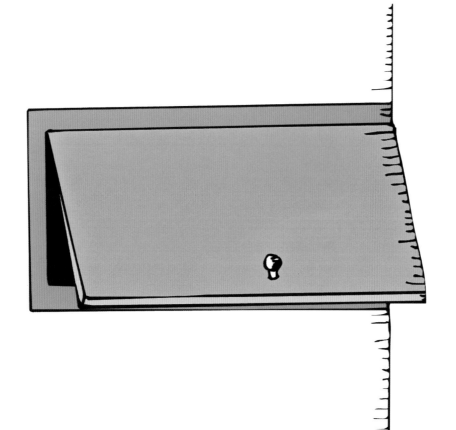

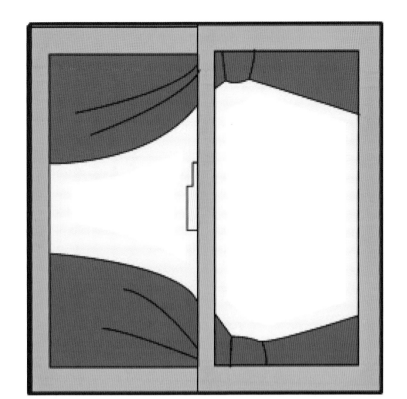

A-8

A-8

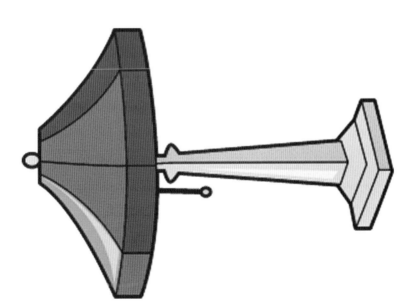

A-9

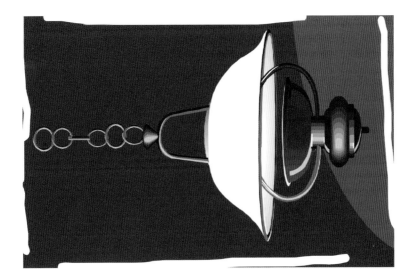

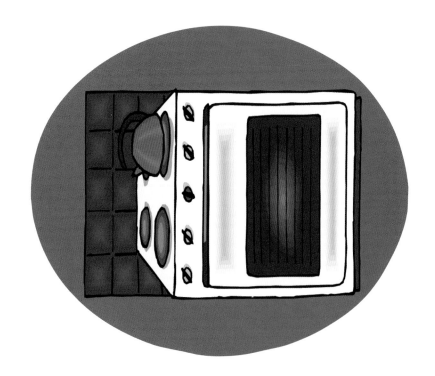

A-12

A-12

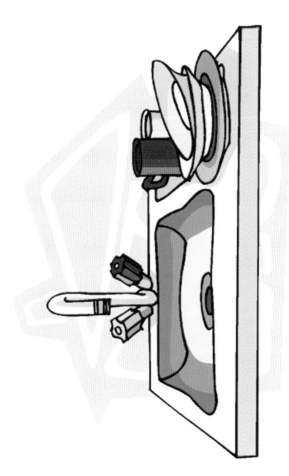

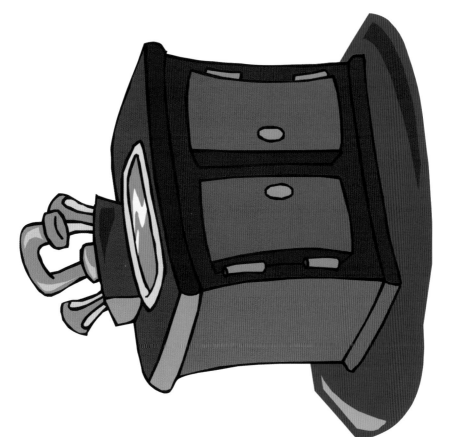

A-13

A-13

A-15

A-15

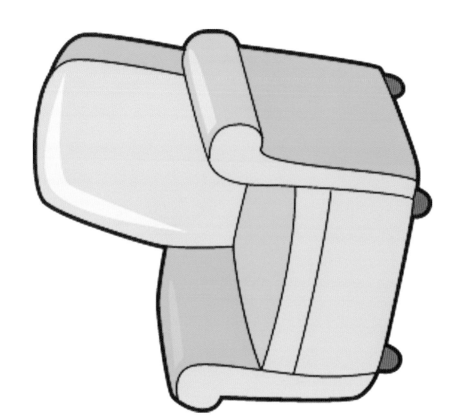

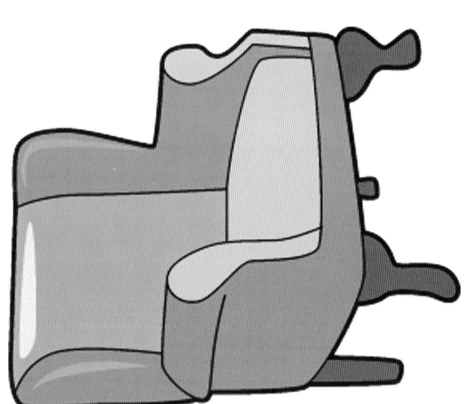

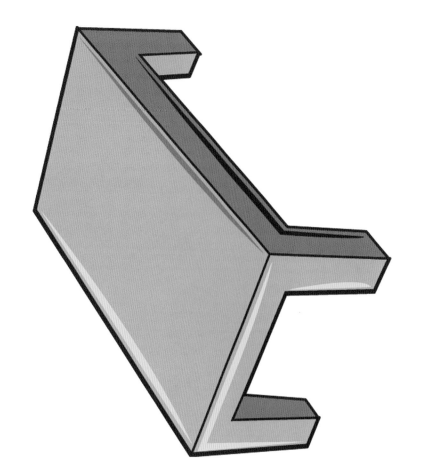

A-17

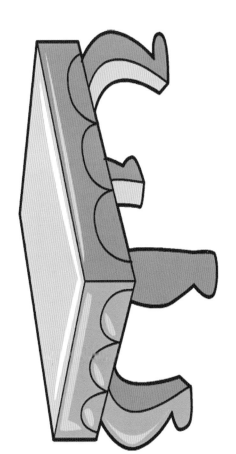

A-17

A-18

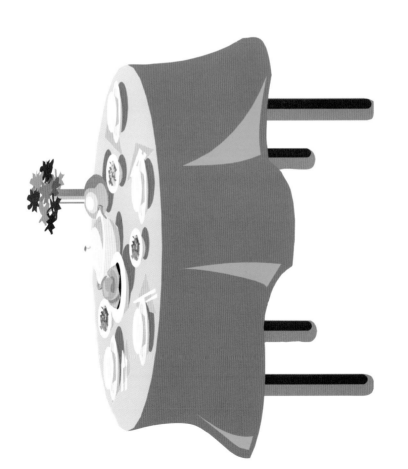

A-18

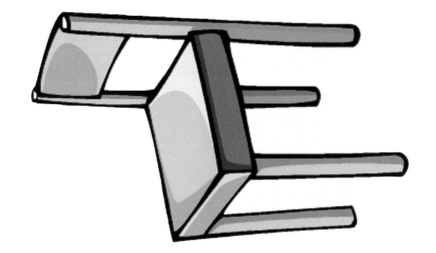

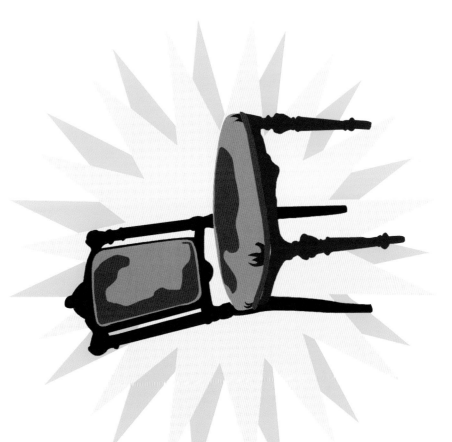

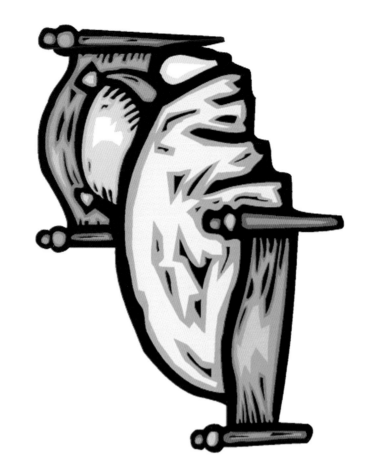

A-20

A-20

A-21

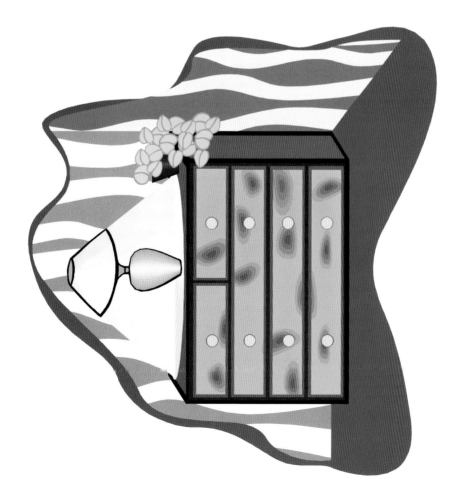

A-21

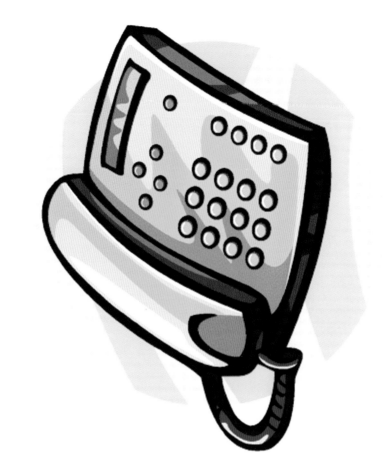

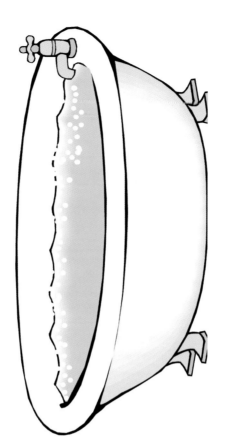

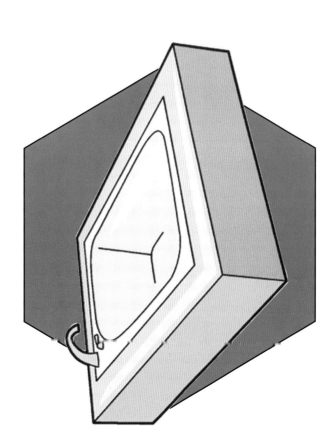

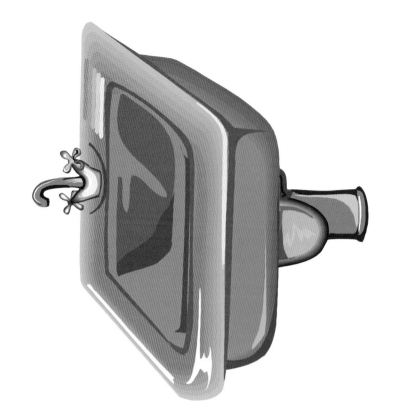

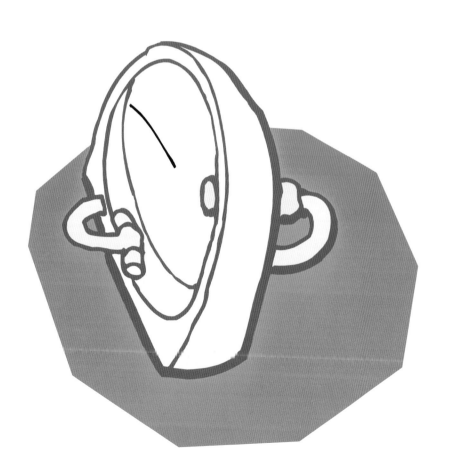

B-1

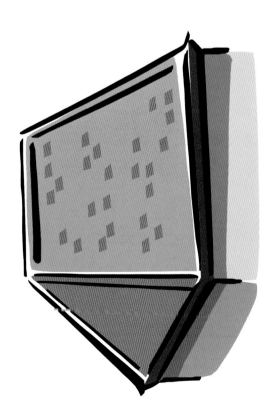

B-1

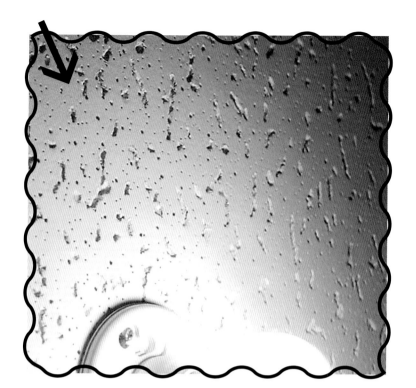

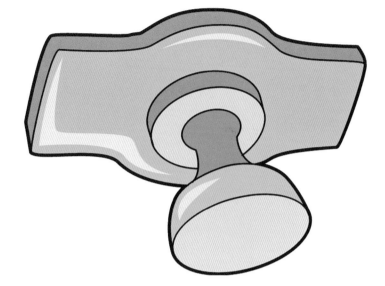

B-5

B-5

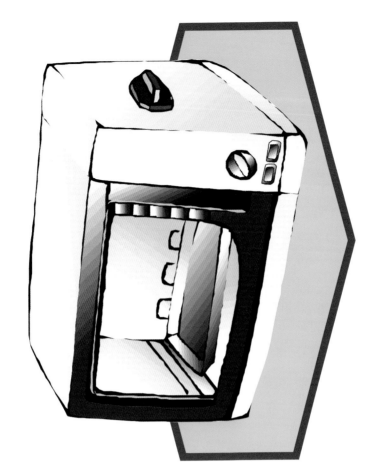

 B-6

 B-6

B-8

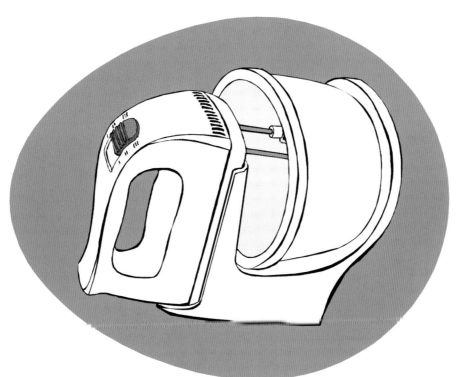

 B-10

 B-10

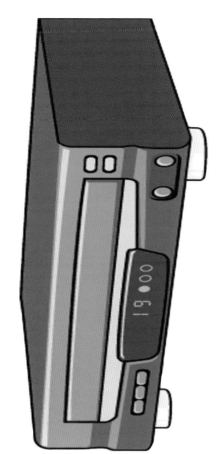

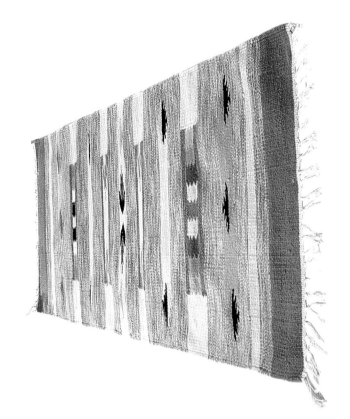

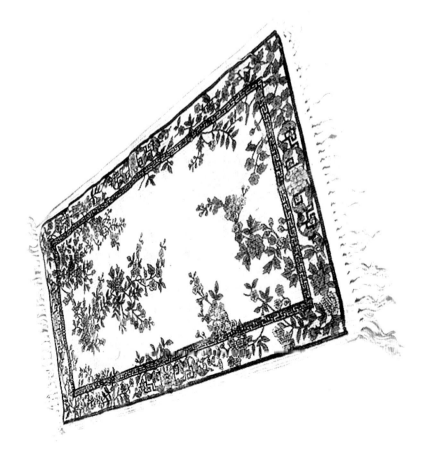

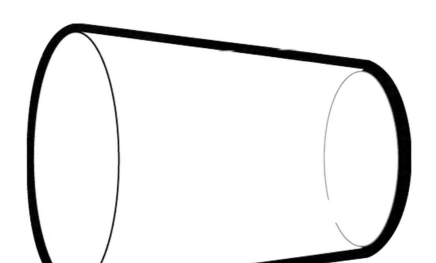

B-15

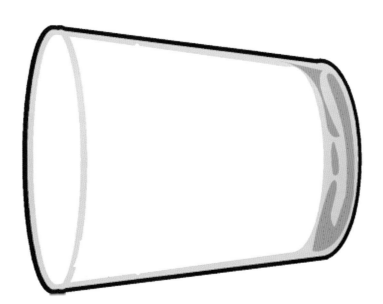

B-15

B-16

B-16

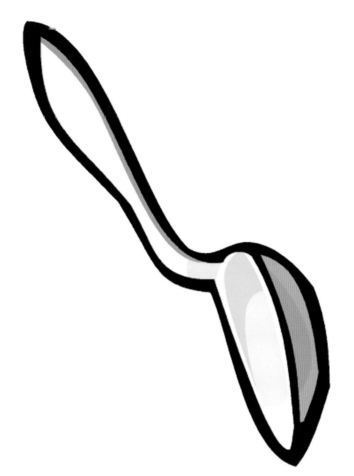

B-17

B-17

B-19

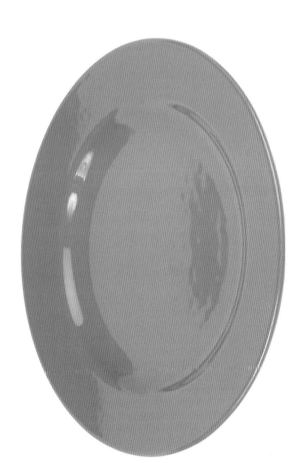

B-19

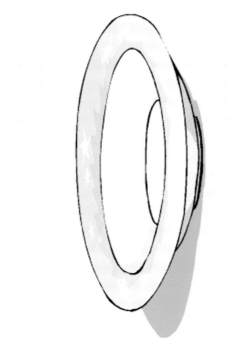

 B-21

 B-21

B-22

B-22

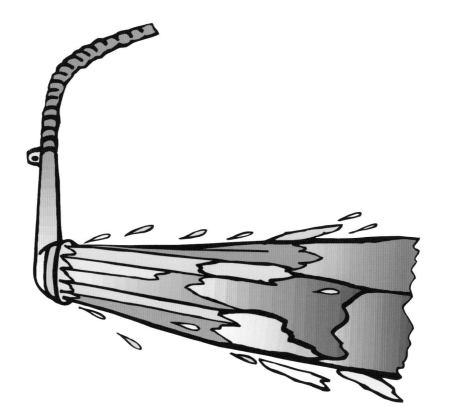

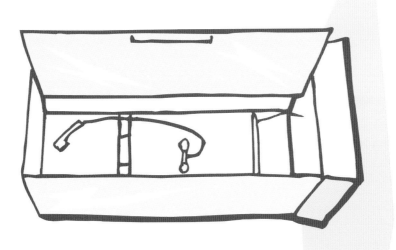

B-24

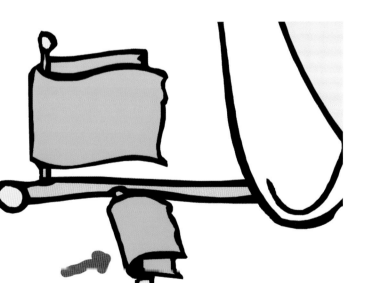

B-24

B-25

B-25

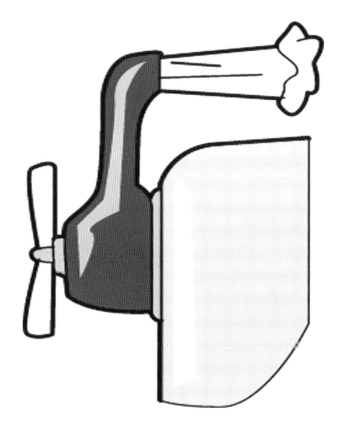

C-2

C-2

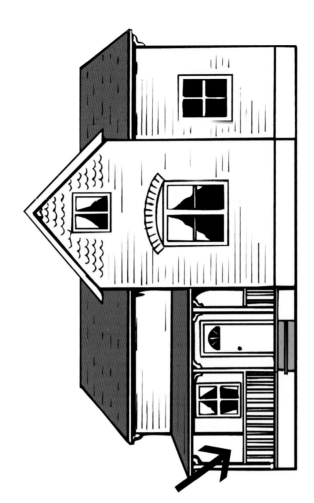

C-4

C-4

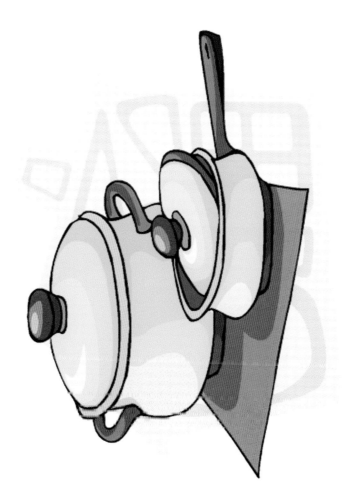

C-6

C-5

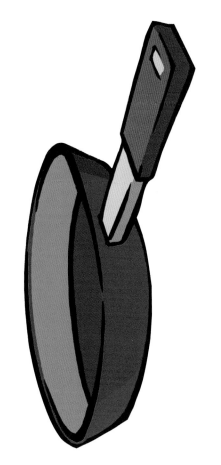

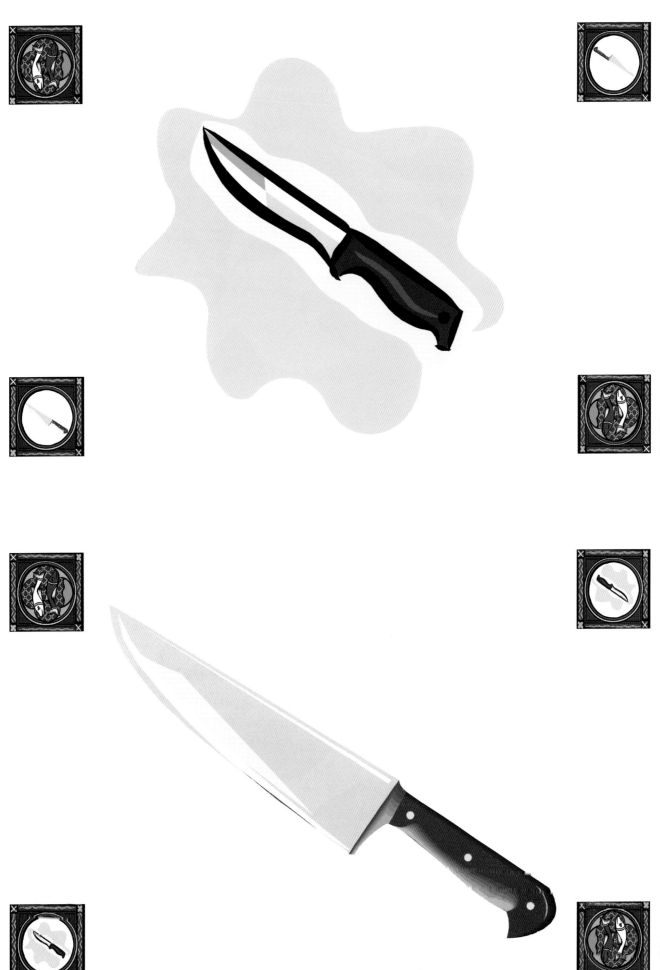

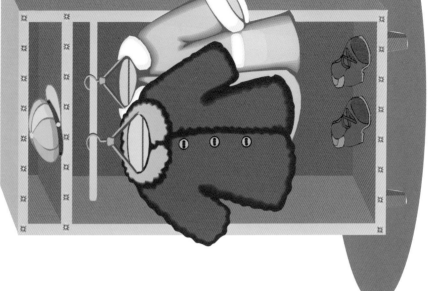

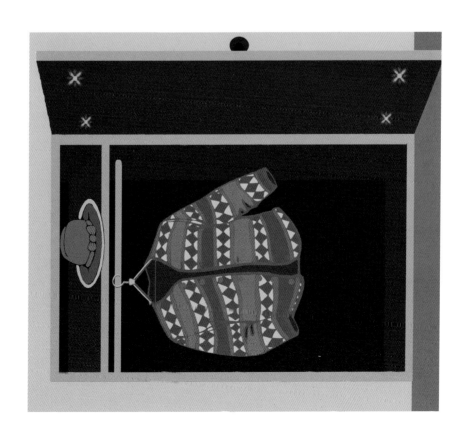

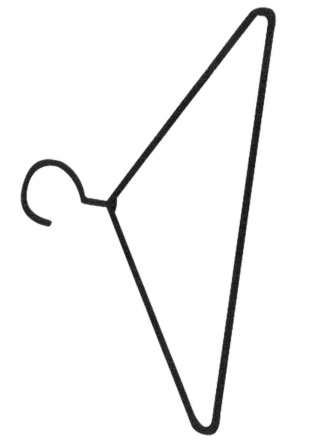

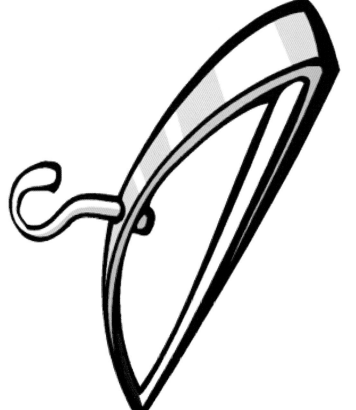

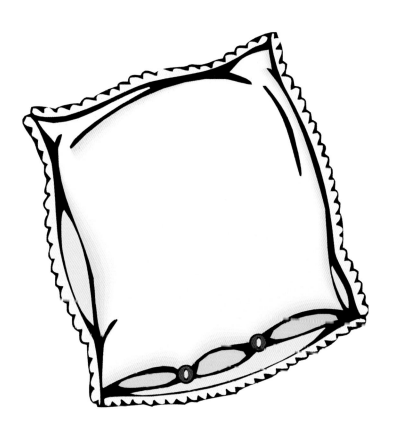

C-12

C-12

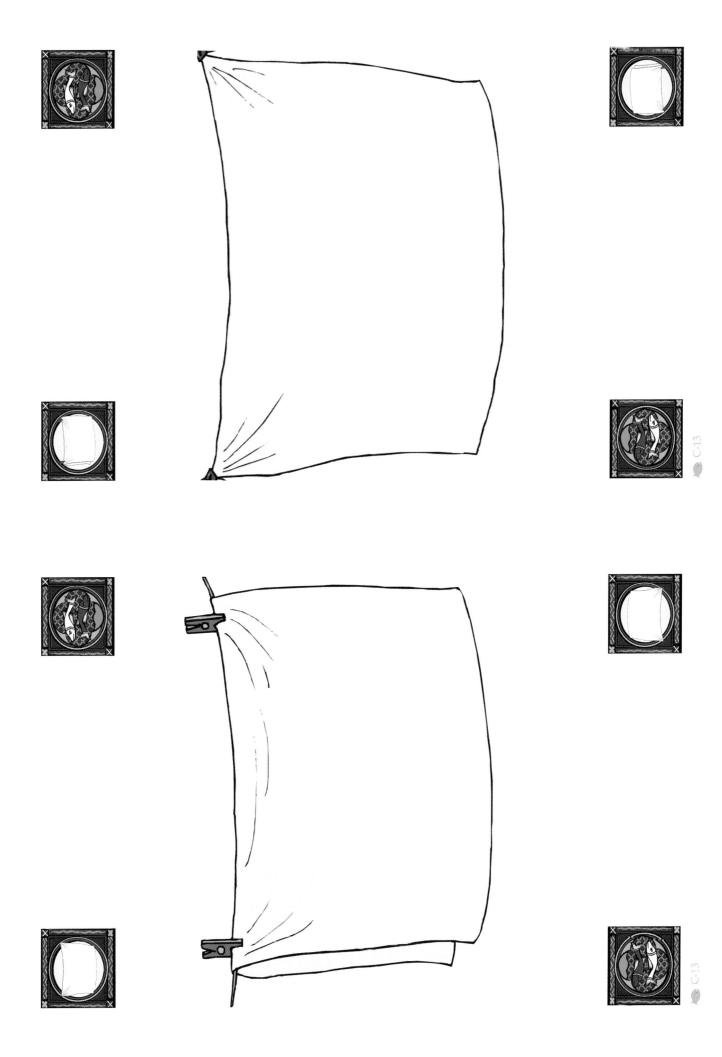

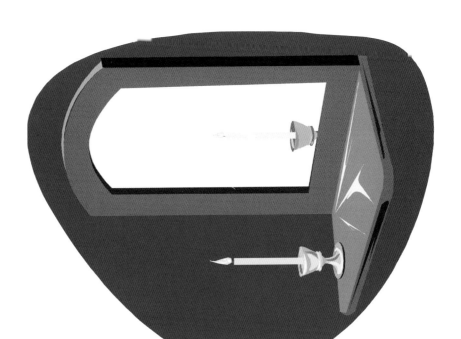

 C-14

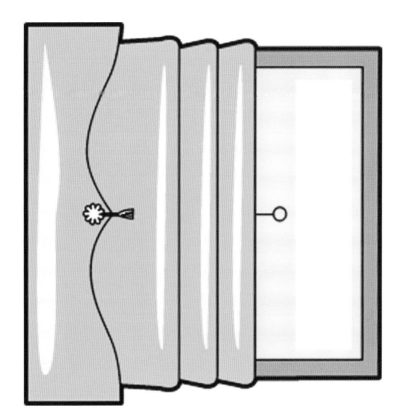

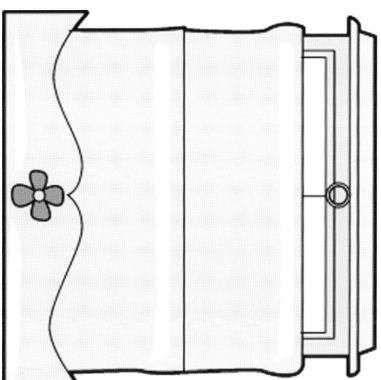

C-18

C-18

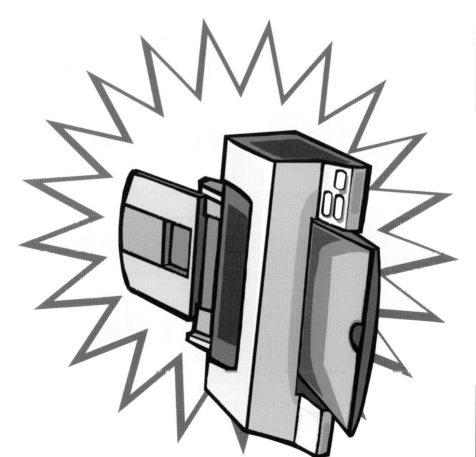

C-19

C-19

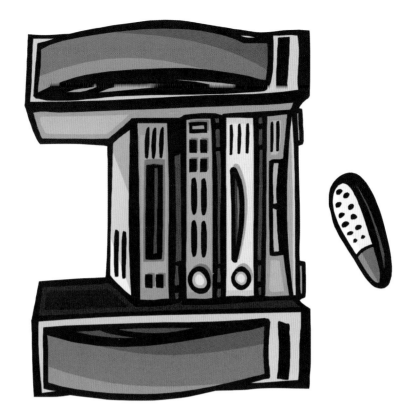

C-21

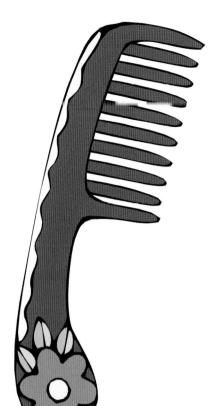

C-22

C-22

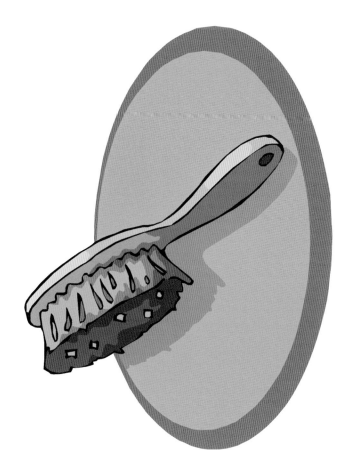

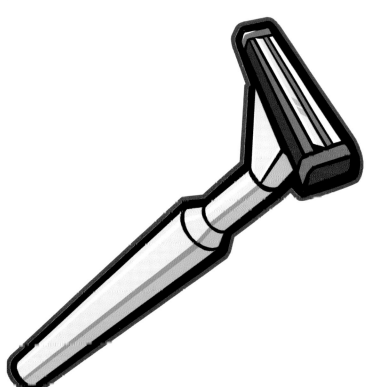

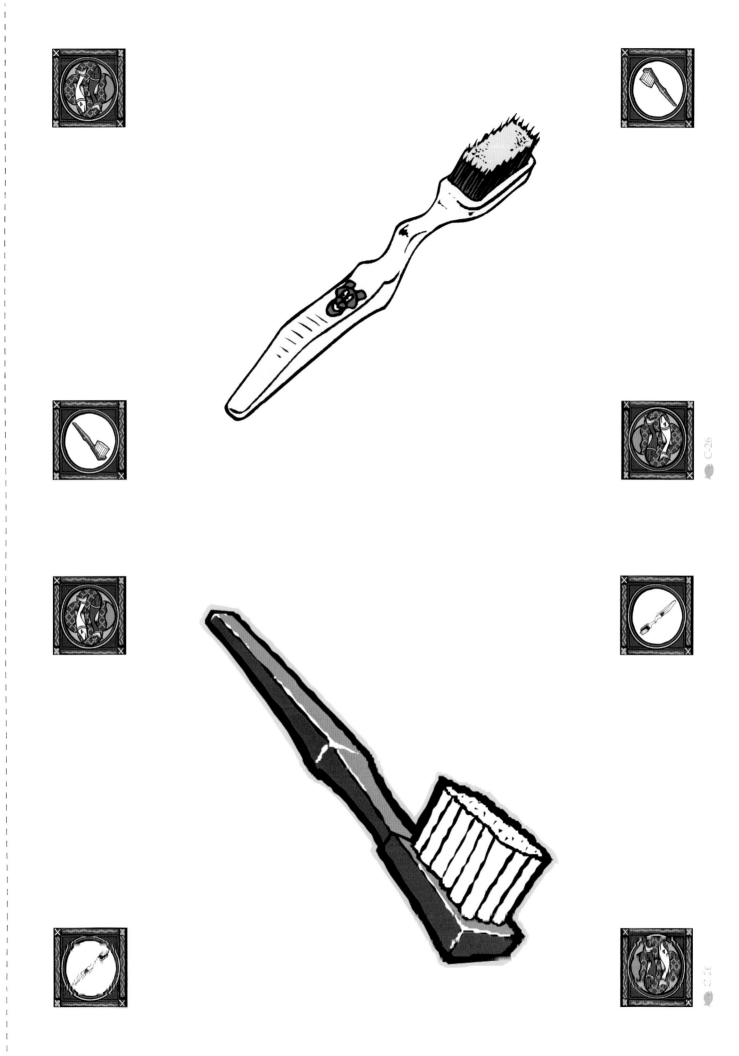

D-1

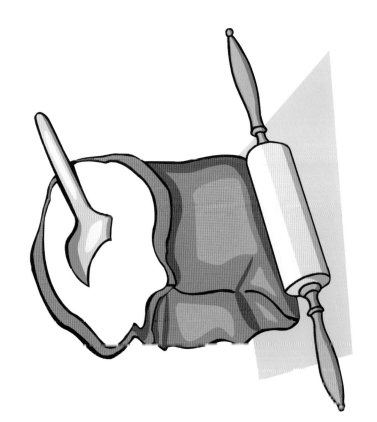

D-

D-2

D-4

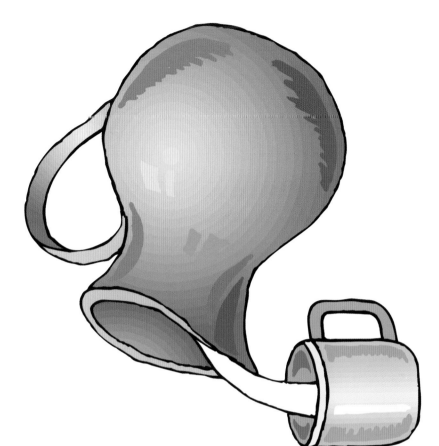

D-3

D-4

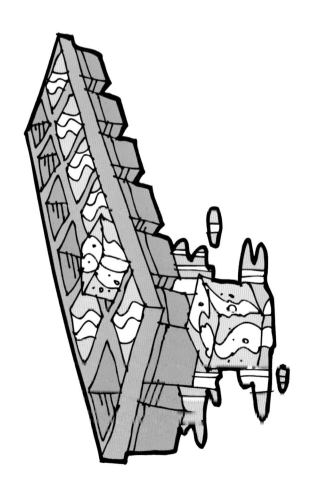

L-4

D-6

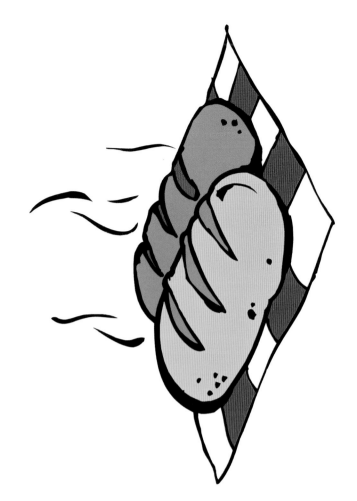

D-6 🐟

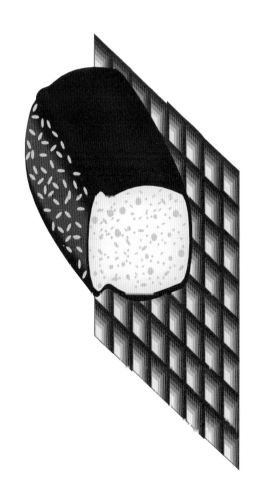

D-5 🐟

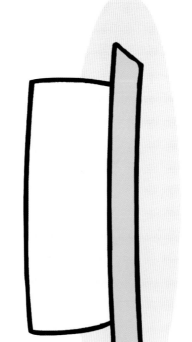

D-7

D-7

D-8

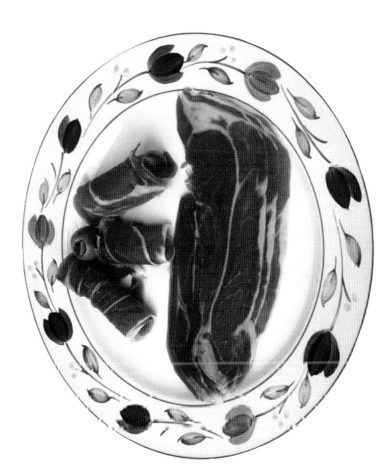

D-

Additional Vocabulary

To make pairs of cards, photocopy these pages and cut out the pictures and paste them on blank cards.

173

Additional vocabulary, 1: tea kettle, teapot, candle, fireplace, coffee pot, pepper grinder and salt shaker, blender, bottle, coffee maker, picture/painting, toothpaste, fan, electric outlet and cord with plug, high chair, portable stereo/boombox, rocking chair, window curtain, garden/flowers, flower pot, trowel, swing, watering can, hose, tree.

Additional vocabulary, 2: hammer, screwdriver, drill, measuring tape, file, plane, paint brush, saw, step ladder, axe/hatchet, scissors, ladder, dustpan and brush, mop, pail, vacuum cleaner, broom, shovel, rake, pitch fork, wheel barrow, hoe, clipper/pruner, lawn mower.

Five, 30-minute lessons for Go Fish

Monday

1. Vocabulary / Pronunciation

- Select one set of 52 cards (26 words).

- Show each word to the students and say the word.

- Flash the cards in random order and ask them to identify the objects.

- Check individuals for the correct pronunciation.

2. Speaking

- Divide the cards among the learners.

- Ask the first person, ***"What do you have?"***

- Demonstrate the answer, ***I have a ...***

- Get the first person to ask the same question of the next person
  and so on.

- Go around the room until the learners identify all their cards.

- Exchange cards and repeat.

- Pay special attention to pronunciation.

3. Spelling

- Divide the students into two teams.

- Pick a card from the deck, say the word, and ask everyone
  to write it down.

- Ask one person from each team to spell out the word orally
  or write the word on the board.

- Keep score on the blackboard, one point for each word spelled correctly.

177

Tuesday

1. Vocabulary / Grammar

- Introduce new vocabulary: card, shuffle, deck, deal, pair

- Introduce new sentences:

  Do you have a _____? Yes, I do / No, I don't.

  I have a pair. Pick up a card.

  It's your/my turn.

  You're the winner.

- Explain the rules of the game if your students can understand verbal explanations. It may be easier to "play" a sample game, walking through the sequence of plays with each player as the game unfolds.

2. Speaking / Conversation

- Play a game.

- Use the following format:

  Do you have a _____?

  Yes, I do.

  No, I don't. Go Fish.

- Encourage the players to include names.

  Carlos, do you have a _____?

  No, I don't. Go Fish, Mariko!

3. Spelling

- Read each word aloud (include new vocabulary from above).

- Ask the learners to write down each word.

- Collect the papers to check accuracy and progress.

Wednesday

1. Grammar / Singular & Plural

- Show the learners a card and say, **"I have a _____,"** placing emphasis on the word "a" or use the word "one."
- Hold up the matching card and say, **"I have two _____,"** placing emphasis on the word "two" and the plural suffix.

2. Pronunciation / Spelling

- Say each word as a plural, emphasizing the sound of the plural suffix.
- Explain the different ending sounds of plural words: /s, /z/, and /iz/.
    > Note that only **switch, couch, garage, porch, glass, brush** take the /iz/ sound.
- On the blackboard, ask the learners to group the plural words according to their final ending sounds.

3. Speaking / Conversation

- Play a game. Increase the difficulty by expanding the sentences:

    PLAYER 1 **Do you have a _____?**

    PLAYER 2 **Yes, I have a _____.**

    PLAYER 1 **Thank you. Now I have a pair of _____.**

    PLAYER 2 **No, I don't have a ____ . Go Fish!**

- Pay special attention to the pronunciation of plural words

179

Thursday

1. Vocabulary

- Introduce new vocabulary with a new set of cards.
- Ask the learners to categorize the objects according to room.

    (Some of the objects will be found in more than

    one room - encourage discussion)

2. Grammar / Speaking / Spelling / Reading

- Pick a card and read it aloud (*e.g.* toaster).
- On the blackboard write, ***"There is a toaster in the kitchen."***
- Show the second toaster card and write, ***"There are two toasters in the kitchen."***
- Pick up another card and read it aloud.
- Ask the first student to follow your example, writing their answer

    on the board (ask others to help if the student has difficulty spelling).

- Ask the student to read the sentence aloud.
- Now this student picks the next card and reads it aloud, and the second

    student must write their answer, and so on.

3. Writing / Grammar / Spelling

- Bring in pictures of different rooms.
- Ask the students to write short sentences about each picture,

    (*e.g.* There is/are _____ in the kitchen.).

Friday

1. Grammar

- Teach variations of ***Do you have a _____?***

  Would you have a _____?

  Are you holding a _____?

  I think you have a _____. Do you?

  I would like a _____.

  I'd like a _____.

  I need a _____.

2. Speaking / Conversation

- Play ***Go Fish*** with a mixture of cards from the two sets you have used.

- Encourage the students to use the variations above.

3. Listening / Writing / Spelling

- Read several short sentences to the students.

- Ask the students to write each sentence (give sufficient time before you read the next sentence).

  Some examples:

  > ***I have a toaster.***
  > ***John has two forks. (use student names)***
  > ***Do you have a knife?***
  > ***Yes, I have a comb.***
  > ***No, I don't have a brush.***
  > ***There are two plates.***
  > ***There is a lamp.***
  > ***I would like a glass.***
  > ***Is there a fridge?***
  > ***Are there windows?***

- *(Time permitting)* Play one of the other games
  (***Match It, Bingo, Pantomime, etc.***)

Resources

Index Card Games for ESL. 7 game techniques using index cards give practice with vocabulary, grammar, pronunciation, speaking, listening. Photocopyable material is appropriate for students at different proficiency levels.

Match It! Another photocopyable collection of index card games. The game "Match It!" is similar to "Concentration." The materials range in difficulty from basic/easy to advanced/difficult.

Pronunciation Card Games. A photocopyable collection of index card games working on minimal pairs, syllabification, stress, and intonation.

The Great Big Bingo Book. A photocopyable collection of bingo games, providing practice with grammar, vocabulary, writing, pronunciation, and cultural information.

Shenanigames. 49 games practicing specific grammar points of graded difficulty. They are appropriate for students from middle school to adult.

Superphonic Bingo: Breaking the Sounds Barrier – Fun with Phonics for Spelling and Literacy. 15 photocopyable games, each with 8 different cards, practice the phonic system of English. These Bingo games complement the text, **From Sound to Sentence: Learning to Read and Write English – Basic Literacy and Spelling, Phonics and Sight Words**, an amusing, easy-to-use beginning or remedial literacy text.

Stress Rulz! Learning/practicing the rules of stress using Rap music on CD.

The ESL Miscellany. A single-volume teacher resource book with dozens of lists of grammatical information, vocabulary topics, cultural information, miscellaneous material (punctuation rules, spelling rules, abbreviations, maps, gestures, etc.). A great resource for developing games and other lesson materials.

Lexicarry. Hundreds of uncaptioned pictures which get students talking about language, learning vocabulary, and discussing what language is appropriate in the pictured situations. Includes functions, sequences, operations, topics, and proverbs. Ideal for pair and small group work. A word list in the back allows for self-study. Wordlists in other languages and a teacher's guide are free at www.Lexicarry.com. Over 4500 words.

English Interplay: Surviving. A first text for beginning adolescents and adults. Students work in pairs, triads, and small groups, learning basic grammar, spelling, pronunciation, numbers, and a 700-word vocabulary.

Pro Lingua Associates • 800-366-4775 • www.ProLinguaAssociates.com